Relaxation

The complete manual for a calm and healthy life

igloobooks

Published in 2015
by Igloo Books Ltd
Cottage Farm
Sywell
NN6 0BJ
www.igloobooks.com

Cover designed by Nicholas Gage
Interiors designed by Charles Wood-Penn
Edited by Natalie Baker

LEO002 1015
2 4 6 8 10 9 7 5 3 1
ISBN 978-1-78557-049-0

Cover image: Anya Berkut / iStock
Interior images: iStock

Printed and manufactured in China

Contents

Introduction

Relax! Easy to say, but very hard to do. Relaxation is a skill that you can learn and practise.

Relaxation of body and mind allows us to let go of the stresses and strains of the day, of our worries, our fears and tiredness. It allows us to nourish and replenish mind and body so that we are better able to meet and enjoy the challenges of life.

This book is a guide through different relaxation techniques and strategies. Explore the different methods and find the one that best suits you. There are relaxation techniques that involve quiet sitting or lying and exercises, including t'ai chi and yoga.

The relaxation techniques are appropriate for everyone, of any age or physical fitness level. Make modifications wherever you feel appropriate.

Any new skill takes practice, and learning how to relax fully is something that most of us are not used to. Try whichever technique you choose for at least a few weeks, to begin to feel the full benefit. Part of the process of learning to relax fully using the methods outlined here is allowing it to be difficult. If you struggle to sit for five minutes, let alone ten, then sit for four and build up gradually. Don't beat yourself up about it. You are learning to let go, not add to your tension.

What is relaxation? Some people will say it's going out for a drink with friends or going to the movies and sharing a bag of popcorn. These are relaxing and fun things to do, but they do not activate a harmonised body–mind relaxation. Lying on the sofa watching TV and eating chocolate biscuits is indulgent and restful, but again it does not initiate active relaxation.

Full and active relaxation involves quietness and stillness in body and mind. It actually rejuvenates and energises the body. It comes from a relaxation practice that focuses on consciously and deliberately letting your mind and body release tension. This deep relaxation helps you let go of the chatter that goes on in the mind. It clears a space for you to just be. There is plenty of other time to let your mind be busy and full of chatter.

In order to fully relax and feel both the physiological and emotional benefits, we need to stimulate the body's natural and instinctive relaxation response. The active relaxation techniques in this book show you how. There are many methods. What's important is to find one that suits you. You can only find out which one will be most effective for you by trying them out. There are strategies, too, to help you gain a positive relaxation balance in your work and home life.

Sometimes, we feel so tense and stressed that the idea of relaxation adds to the pressure we feel, but taking five minutes to let go of the tension in your body or mind will be nourishing and rewarding.

Relaxation techniques can be done anywhere, anytime, except when driving or using machinery because they can make you feel a bit sleepy.

CHAPTER 1

The Importance of Relaxation

Life is full of surprises and exciting challenges. It is full of stress and anxieties, too. Having a young family or a new job is exciting and wonderful but it can also be a source of exhaustion and tension. Active relaxation helps us manage stress before it becomes overwhelming. This is hugely important for maintaining mental and physical well-being.

Stress can be positive. It helps push us towards new directions and deal with new situations. However, too much stress can put a strain on our emotional health, which can affect our physical health.

Relaxation techniques and tools help slow down the body and mind. Practised regularly, relaxation allows the mind to let go of the anxieties and stresses that build up. It allows the body to release physical tensions. Some techniques focus on the body and others on the mind. The effect of all the techniques is to help connect and harmonise the body and mind. As the body lets go and the mind empties, the effect of relaxation is to replenish and energise the body and mind, enabling us to enjoy and cope better with life's ups and downs.

Take a moment to reflect. Can you identify any particular triggers for stress and tension in your life? What makes your shoulders tighten and your jaw clench? Can you identify other ways that stress makes you feel?

Reflect on what you do to counteract stress and tension. If it's not possible to address the cause, then it is certainly possible to address the effect. You might feel that you don't have time to relax, but if you invest in relaxation you will find yourself recharged and more able to deal effectively with what life presents.

If you are not convinced about the physiological benefits of relaxation, read on.

You are probably familiar with the immediate physical effect of stress – a sudden rush and scramble of feelings, dry mouth, nausea and fast breathing. These responses are caused by an increased heart rate and a rise in blood pressure. This is the 'fight or flight' response from the body as it works out whether to attack the problem or run from it. This response helps to keep you safe and is triggered by part of the autonomic nervous system, called the sympathetic nervous system. But over time, the physiological effect of this fight or flight response can have an impact on health. It raises cholesterol levels and depresses the immune system. Stress is generally acknowledged as a factor in ill-health.

In the 1970s, cardiologist Herbert Benson identified the relaxation response. This refers to changes that occur in the body when it is in a state of deep relaxation. These changes include a decrease in blood pressure and heart rate and a reduction in stress hormones. This all contributes to an increased feeling of calm and control. The effects of the relaxation response help counter the negative effects of the fight or flight response. Consciously stimulating this part of the nervous system, the parasympathetic nervous system, kick starts the body's relaxation response. The following relaxation techniques do just this!

It doesn't take much effort to have a lie-in in the morning or flop in front of the TV. It can feel good and there is nothing wrong with it. However, if you want to reap the benefits of deeper relaxation, a union of physical and mental release, it takes a conscious effort and application. It's most effective when practised regularly.

People have practised relaxation techniques for thousands of years. The habit and practise of these ancient natural skills has too often been buried by the business of modern life. It's time to unearth them and tune in to the relaxation state that brings balance and harmony to body and mind.

The active relaxation techniques in this book focus on meditative and breathing relaxation and on the exercises practised in the ancient arts of yoga and t'ai chi. The meditative techniques in this book are not influenced by any religious or other set of beliefs. They are for anyone to enjoy and benefit from.

Doctors and health professionals increasingly suggest relaxation techniques such as meditation to help with a range of physical and mental health issues. However, if you have any health concerns, check with your doctor first. If you feel any negative effects from the practices, talk to your doctor.

Relaxation techniques can make you feel sleepy and you may find you nod off sometimes. You will feel greater benefits if you practise on an empty stomach and you may also find the sitting or lying positions are more comfortable.

Make your relaxation time special – a practice to enjoy. A scented candle, or burning some of your favourite essential oils (see pages 90–91) creates a calm and peaceful atmosphere. Set up an area for your relaxation – mark it out with some flowers in a jar or arrange some pebbles or leaves on a small tray or plate. Have a clock or timer nearby to avoid spending your relaxation time trying to work out how long you have left.

In some of these exercises, especially mindfulness and breathing meditation, it is useful to be seated. Sitting still can present its own physical challenges and niggles. It is worth really looking at your sitting posture to make sure it is giving you the best base for relaxation.

When you start, it can feel very difficult to sit still while doing nothing except focusing on . . . nothing. You will find it becomes easier with practice, and that you can incorporate awareness of your body into the practice.

An easy cross-legged position gives a good foundation as the folded legs provide a stable base. Energy can flow and remain centred when your back is straight and your shoulders are straight and relaxed. Roll up a blanket or use a cushion to sit on if that feels more comfortable. There are several ways in which you can hold your hands. You could have them resting on your lap with fingers gently interlocked or with one hand resting on top of the other, palms upwards. Or have them in a position with the tips of the thumb and index finger of each hand lightly touching, with hands resting upwards on each knee.

If you are flexible, you might be able to sit in full or half lotus. In this position, your legs root your body and hold your upper body as a strong stem.

If you are not used to sitting for any length of time in these seated positions, you may find it difficult at first. Avoid stressing about it. Perhaps start in the cross-legged position to allow your focus to be on the relaxation practice and not on the discomfort you feel.

If you prefer, sit on a hard-backed chair. Plant your feet firmly on the ground. Drop the shoulders and lift the back. Keep your head aligned with your spine, with your chin very slightly dropped down. If possible, take off your glasses or take out your contact lenses.

CHAPTER 2

Full Muscle Relaxation

Sometimes, we are so used to being tense that we think it is our natural state and are unaware of the stress we hold. It's time to get back in touch with your natural relaxed body. Deep muscle relaxation helps you notice the difference between stressed and relaxed muscles. Once you are able to notice signs of stress in your muscles, you can begin to relax them.

In this deep muscle relaxation, you deliberately and consciously tense and tighten specific muscles and areas of the body. Then you release them.

The part of the body you are tensing may shake a little but it should not hurt. If a muscle group hurts, leave that area out. It helps to visualise all the body parts that make up the area you are tensing and relaxing. For instance, when focusing on a foot, think of the top, the ball, the big toe, the little toe, the heel, the ankle bone, etc.

Choose a time when you will not be disturbed for at least 10 minutes. Choose a quiet place that is neither too hot nor too cold. Wear loose comfortable clothing, without shoes. Wear socks if that suits you.

Lie on your back on a mat. If you feel discomfort in your lower back, bend your legs with feet hip-width apart. Arms are by your sides. Allow your neck to lengthen and gently close your eyes.

Allow your breathing to be natural, noticing the rise and fall of your belly. Try to let everything fall away as you breathe out and breathe in fresh, rejuvenating oxygen.

Work your way up the whole of the body, isolating the right side of any muscle or area first, and then the left. As you tense, you can slightly lift the part of the body you are tensing off the ground (for instance your foot, leg or hand). If you do this, gently release it back to the ground rather than crashing to the floor with a thump. Hold the tension for at least two seconds. Remember to breathe throughout.

Start by bringing your focus to your toes, feet and ankles. Breathe in, scrunch your toes, and tighten and tense the balls of the feet, the heels and the ankles. Really think about tensing all of the tiny cells and fibres in your toes and feet. Squeeze and hold for a couple of seconds, then release. Let your feet and all the muscles in your feet go floppy.

Bring your focus to the front of your legs. Point your feet and feel the tightness in your shins and the large muscles in your thighs. Tense and hold. Let it go.

Bring your focus to the back of your legs. Flex your feet, pushing your heels down into the floor. Tighten the back of your thighs. Tense and hold. Let it go.

Turn your awareness to your bottom. Clench and hold. Release. Notice how your lower body feels.

Focus on your hands. Inhale as you clench your fists. Hold them tight. Think about tightening your fingers, squeeze and feel the tension. Then, let go. Consciously, let all the tension flow away from your fingers, knuckles, fists and wrists. Exhale as you let go of the tension. It can help to say silently to yourself 'relax' or 'let go' as you release.

Notice your breathing as your muscles become floppy and limp. Notice how your hands and fingers feel.

Draw your mind to your lower arms and elbows. Tense and squeeze. Then release. Notice your breathing. Notice the feeling as the muscles soften into the mat if you are lying on the floor.

Now draw your attention to your upper arms. Tense and squeeze. Then release. (Remember to complete this on both the right and left sides of the body.)

Bring your focus to the chest area. Notice the rise and fall of your chest as you breathe gently. Inhale and consciously tense the chest area. Then soften and release on an exhale. Breathe gently.

Shoulders often hold a lot of tension and tightness. Inhale as you lift, squeeze and tighten them. It's quite a noticeable movement. Then exhale and let them drop. Let them soften and roll back gently.

Draw your shoulder blades towards each other behind your back. Contract. Hold. Release.

Draw your attention to your neck. Avoid lifting it. Simply try to tense the muscles in the neck. Let go.

Bring your focus to the jaw and face. Inhale. Scrunch up your nose, lips, cheeks and eyes. Accentuate the tension that is probably already in your clenched jaw and tongue as it presses against the roof of the mouth. Hold and then release as you exhale. Notice how your face and jaw feel now.

Lift your eyebrows and focus on holding tension in the head. Let it go.

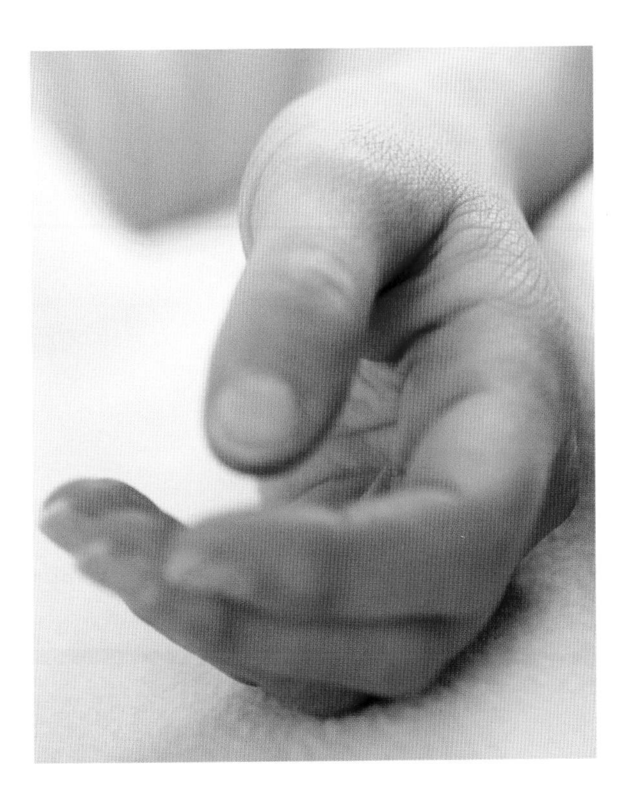

Allow your body to sink into the mat, supported by the ground. Let your muscles enjoy the relaxation as it flows through your body from the top of your head to the tips of your toes.

When you are ready, gently wiggle your toes and fingers to bring back movement to the body. Roll onto your right side and stay in a gently curled foetal position for a few moments. Slowly sit up. Pause before you stand up, enjoying the positive energy that you have generated.

To begin with, practise the full body muscle relaxation for a few weeks. Once you are familiar with it, adapt it by focusing on a particular area of the body, not just one muscle. For instance, tense both legs at the same time, or the chest and shoulders.

Shorter variations on the muscle relaxation can easily be fitted into a busy day at home or work. Aim to continue with the full body muscle relaxation regularly to gain maximum benefit. Practise this form of relaxation even when you are not feeling particularly stressed – it is all about maintaining balance between body and mind.

You can also work on the 'letting go' part of the practice instead of consciously tensing the muscles beforehand.

This is a more subtle release of tension as your muscles relax from their natural state. Do this paying full attention to how your muscles feel after relaxing them. Work through the whole body in this way or on particular muscle groups.

It is common to find your mind wandering away from the conscious tense and relax pattern. That's fine. Just gently bring your attention back to the body. Remember to breathe naturally. It can help to listen to guidance, so you may want to practise using a visual or audio recording.

The following script works on both sides of the body at the same time. Allow time for long pauses for the body and mind to respond to the instruction.

"Notice your breathing as your belly rises and falls. Take a deep breath in through your nose, fill your belly and let it rise. Breathe out and allow your belly to drop. As you exhale, imagine releasing any tension in your body, letting it flow away.

[PAUSE]

Focus on your feet. Breathe in as you scrunch your toes. Squeeze the muscles in your feet. Feel the tension. Hold, then as you breathe out, release the tension.

[PAUSE]

Now take your attention to your legs. Notice how they feel.

[PAUSE]

Tighten your shins and your thigh muscles. Tense and hold for two seconds.

[PAUSE]

Let it go.

[PAUSE]

Focus on the backs of your legs. Flex your feet, pushing your heels down. Tighten the backs of your thighs; hold, then let it go.

[PAUSE]

Bring your focus to the front of your legs. Inhale and tighten the muscles. Hold. Let the tension go as you breathe out.

[PAUSE]

Tighten your buttocks. Squeeze and hold. Release. Let your hips drop.

[PAUSE]

Clench and suck in your stomach and then release. Let the tension melt away.

[PAUSE]

Make a fist. Visualise tensing every bone in your hand and wrist. Hold and let go. Let your hands and wrists sink into the ground.

[PAUSE]

Tighten your arms, elbows, triceps and biceps. Hold. Release.

[PAUSE]

Inhale as you lift your shoulders to your ears. Scrunch. Hold and release.

[PAUSE]

Pull your shoulder blades back towards each other. Tense and release.

[PAUSE]

Bring your attention to your face. Clench your jawbone and your mouth. Shut your eyes tight. And let go.

[PAUSE]

Lift your eyebrows as high as possible. Hold. Let go.

[PAUSE]

Feel the softness in your face.

[PAUSE]

Allow a wave of relaxation flow up and down your body."

CHAPTER 3

Relax with Mindfulness

Do you find yourself always planning ahead, letting internal chatter clutter your mind, thinking about two other things as you are doing one thing? It is not easy to stop this habit. Mindful meditation can help.

By drawing attention to the present moment, mindfulness helps bring quiet to the mind, balancing body and mind, bringing emotional calm. It is about focusing on the moment, stilling the chattering mind, letting go and allowing things to be, in order to gain an inner stillness and calm.

Many people are waking up to the benefits of mindfulness. GPs often recommend it to help treat depression and anxiety. Schools are introducing it to the curriculum to help children gain stillness in their day and improve their focus. Companies encourage employees to take up the practice.

The aim of mindfulness is to become fully aware of what is – whatever that is – in the present moment. It is a breathtakingly simple premise but it is not easy to master.

Meditation on the breath

Set aside at least 10 minutes a day. Early morning is a good time. Yes, you need to get up early but soon that will become part of your routine. Choose somewhere quiet and peaceful.

Start with a mindful meditation on the breath. Gently close your eyes.

Sit quietly in a strong sitting position (see pages 14–15). Sit still. Sigh out through your mouth to let go of any stress. Bring your breath back to its natural flow. Notice if you are fidgeting. Notice if your mind is telling you to get up and do something else. Simply observe and note these feelings. Let them go.

Bring the attention to your breath. Notice the rise and fall of your belly as you inhale and exhale. Just let the breath be – don't try to control it. Unless you have a cold, aim to breathe in and out through the nose rather than the mouth. Focus on the breath as it brings freshness into your body and exhale what the body no longer needs.

The more you try to 'train' your mind and empty it, the more busy and chattery it seems to become. Rather than feel stressed about the thoughts that crowd into your mind as you try to focus it, simply let them come and go. Avoid judging yourself or being critical as thoughts come and go. Gently bring your attention back to the focus of your mindfulness. As thoughts flood in, notice what happens to your body and your breath. Do you shift a bit in your position? Do you tense?

You will find yourself planning the evening meal, thinking about a friend, worrying about where your keys are, thinking about how long you have left in this position. Any and every thought is fine. Just notice them, then bring the attention back to the breath. You may find some days that there is barely any attention on the breath but you are beginning to still the mind.

Mindfulness is about being. It is not about doing.

These mindfulness exercises can easily be incorporated into a busy day.

Sit in a comfortable position with a straight spine. Gently close your eyes or lower your gaze. The object of your attention is the body. Visualise your skeletal frame from the feet to the skull. Keep your posture upright and relaxed as you direct your attention to the feet, ankles, knees, thighs, pelvis, fingers, wrists and hands. Connect with the base of the spine, vertebrae by vertebrae, all the way up the spine to the crown of the head. Connect with other parts of the body – the brain, heart, lungs, intestines, kidneys, eyes, nose, ears and tongue.

When you have fully scanned the body, sit tall and still and marvel at the body's ceaseless work as it breathes and repairs itself moment to moment, without any conscious instruction. Visualise yourself as a still strong mountain. Throughout your day, walking or sitting, remind yourself that nothing need shake your posture of strength and dignity.

Take a few moments to be mindful of your face, not thinking about appearance but to draw kind awareness to it. Is your skin tight and tense or relaxed? Does your mouth feel taught or is there a small smile at the corner? Are your eyes heavy or light, are they scrunching or fixed wide? Soften and relax the muscles in the face. For a few moments, feel what it is like to be aware of your face without criticism or judgment.

Visualisation

Try following different sensations, or focus on one particular object. This might be a flickering flame from a candle, or a pebble you picked up from a beach. Place the object in front of you. Allow your eyes to rest softly on the object. Focus on the detail of it. Notice the flicker of the flame or its colour, or pay attention to the shape and texture of the pebble. Allow other thoughts to come in and let them go as your mind focuses back on the object of your gaze.

A lot of time is spent in the head. Reconnecting with the physical body creates a healthy balance between physical and mental activity. Periodically, throughout the day, notice what your body is doing and how it feels. At work, be aware of how you are sitting. You don't need to change anything. Just bring your attention to what the body is doing in the present moment.

Sometimes, just stop for a moment. Remain physically still. If you think, "What am I meant to be doing?", the answer is "nothing". Simply be with whatever is.

Creating a few points of stillness returns you to the present moment.

Mindfulness can be practised every day, every moment, as you are picking up a pen, or drinking a glass of water. Be aware of what you are doing. For instance, as you wash your hands, bring your attention to the water. Bring your attention to the feel of the water on your hands. Let other thoughts come and go and then bring your attention back to the hands.

Walking

This chapter's mindfulness practice makes walking the centre of attention. Full attention is on the action of walking. As you walk, focus on the way the ball of your foot rolls over the ground and the heel lifts off the ground. What happens to the other leg and foot? Take it slowly so you can be mindful of each moment. As you lift the right leg, simply say to yourself, "right". Do this with the left leg, too.

Remain aware of your surroundings but focus on the movement of walking. As thoughts float in and out, let them. Avoid judging them or getting caught up in them. Acknowledge them by naming them. For instance, if you hear people chatting, simply say, "hearing" to yourself. Then, gently bring the focus back to the motion of walking. Focus on one thing at a time. Be in the present moment, not thinking about the past or future, just what you are experiencing now.

Keep your gaze about 1.5 metres in front of you. Decide where you are going to walk. This is not a long walk. It can be up and down a short path. The aim is not the distance but the focus of the mind.

You can do this anywhere. Obviously, it is much easier if you are not walking down a busy street with traffic.

The relaxation effect comes from the focus applied to a small movement and the deliberate letting go of thoughts.

CHAPTER 4

Breathing Relaxation

Breathing is what we do every day 24/7, without thinking. However, it is also a vital tool that you can use for relaxation. With deliberate focus, breathing relaxations can calm and harmonise the body and mind, activating the body's relaxation response.

Breathing techniques help you feel connected to your body – they bring your awareness away from the worries in your head and quiet your mind.

The following breathing exercises should not be stressful – they are meant to be relaxing. However, it can take a bit of time to learn to breathe effectively for relaxation. If you find yourself forgetting what you are doing or lose count of the breath, don't worry. Gently bring the breath back to its natural rhythm and then resume the practice.

Don't hold your breath unless it is part of the relaxation. If you have high blood pressure, never hold your breath. Adapt the practice to suit you.

To start each breathing relaxation, inhale deeply through the nose and sigh out any tension. Make as much noise as you need to. It is about letting go. Sigh out as many times as you need to.

Do not strain with the breathing exercises. If you suffer from any breathing difficulties, talk to your doctor.

Belly breathing

Where do you put your hand when you think about how fast or how slowly you are breathing? Most people put their hands to the chest. However, being a 'belly breather', or breathing from the abdomen, can have a significant impact on relaxation and your health in general.

Deep belly-breathing increases the supply of oxygen to your brain and stimulates the parasympathetic nervous system, which promotes calmness. Shallow breathing does not allow your lungs to fill fully or to maximise the oxygenation of the blood, which is important for good health. Shallow breathing can also trigger the sympathetic nervous system to think the body is in flight or fight mode, and release stress hormones.

Put your hands on your belly (around the belly button). Breathe in and consciously let your belly fill up with air. Your belly rises. As you breathe out, the belly pulls back down and into the back. Lie on the floor and place a book on your belly. Feel and see how it rises and falls if you are breathing deeply with your abdomen. For many people, abdominal breathing is the opposite of how they ordinarily breathe, which involves tensing the abdomen. Belly breathing allows you to inhale more oxygen. If you feel particularly stressed or anxious, try this type of breathing. Notice whether it helps you feel calmer.

It takes quite a bit of practice to get used to this type of breathing. Once you have mastered the sense of the belly lifting as you inhale and sinking as you exhale, you can extend the relaxation breathing with the following exercises.

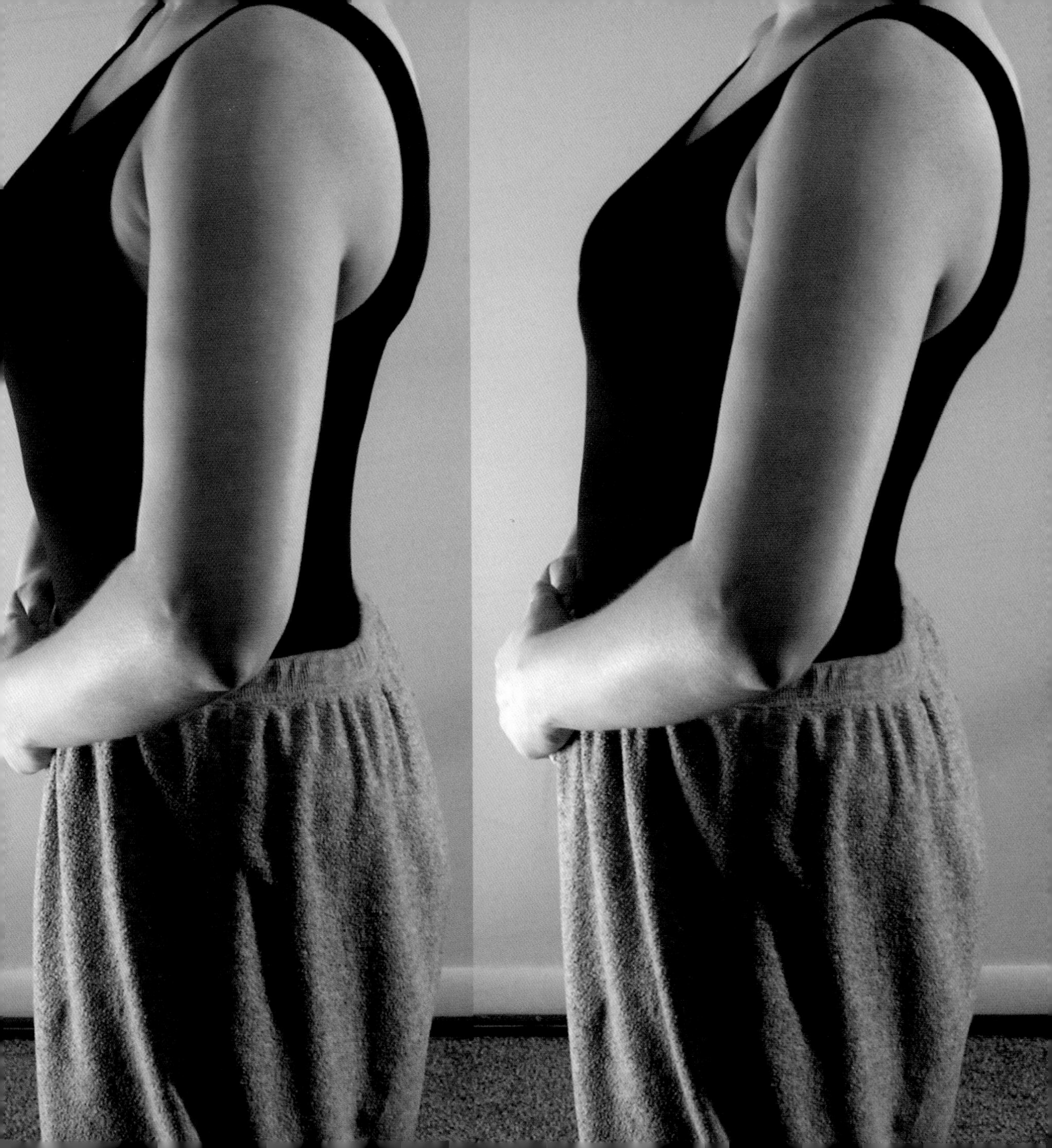

Basic breathing

This simple breathing exercise can prove remarkably difficult. The intention is to still your body and to let your mind focus on a basic count. As your mind flits from one thing to another (anything rather than the count), let it and gently and kindly bring it back to the focus. The trick is to let your mind go where it wants, without judgement or criticism, and when you are aware of it jumping from thought to thought, to softly bring the focus back to the count.

Start by sitting still. Close your eyes gently, or half close your eyes and focus on a spot in front of you. Breathe at your natural rhythm through your nose.

Then, inhale for a count of two. Momentarily hold your breath. Then exhale gently for a count of two. Inhale and repeat the pattern for at least five minutes. You are most likely to find that you lose count or your mind wanders off to plan what you are having for supper or an email you forgot to send. That's fine. Consciously bring the focus back to counting the breath, in and out for a count of two.

Remind yourself to drop your shoulders, and sit tall. Let your jaw slacken (notice if your tongue is tense and curled – let it go).

In your next practice, breathe in and out for a count of three. Do not extend the breath, either on the inhale or exhale, for longer than you feel comfortable with.

Daily practice

The vagus nerve runs from the neck to the diaphragm. This long nerve is key to stimulating the body's relaxation response. It carries signals between the brain and different body systems including those that regulate heart rate and blood pressure. Extending an exhale longer than an inhale, you can indirectly stimulate the vagus nerve to activate the parasympathetic part of the nervous system.

Hold the breath in for a count of one.
Exhale gently for a count of two.
Hold the breath for a count of one.
Make sure you keep your body strong but not tense. Consciously drop your shoulders. Loosen your jaw and tongue. Wriggle on your cushion or mat if you need to.
Keep your breathing even and smooth.
If you can, repeat this for 10 minutes.
Gently acknowledge any thoughts and then find your count again. You may need to breathe at your natural rhythm for a few breaths before picking up the count.

In the following practices, increase the count to two on an inhale and four on an exhale. Decide before you start what the count is so there is no dialogue in your mind about what numbers to count as you are trying to do so. If you find the longer breaths are making you feel stressed, return to slightly shorter ones.

Set a timer and breathe this way for at least five minutes. Once you are used to it, aim for 10 minutes every day as a regular practice.

When you finish, notice any change in your mood or any changes in how your body feels. Open your eyes, gently bring movement back to your body by wriggling your fingers and toes, and carefully rolling your head clockwise and anticlockwise (as long as this does not cause discomfort).

Alternate nostril breathing

Alternate nostril breathing is an effective breathing exercise that brings calm and balance, and unites the right and left sides of the brain. Practise this only once you feel comfortable with the previous breathing relaxations. Do not hold your breath if you have high blood pressure or any breathing difficulties.

Establish a strong, comfortable sitting position.

Use your right hand. Tuck your index and middle finger into your palm. Place your thumb by your right nostril and your ring and little finger by your left nostril.

1. Close the right nostril with your right thumb and inhale through the left nostril.

2. With your ring finger, close off the left nostril.

3. Hold your breath for a short pause.

4. Release the thumb from the right nostril, and exhale through the right nostril, keeping the left nostril closed with your ring finger.

5. Inhale through the right nostril, keeping the left closed.

6. Close both nostrils and hold for a pause.

7. Breathe out through the left nostril, keeping the right closed with the thumb.

8. This is one round. Continue the pattern, inhaling through the left, holding, exhaling through the right, inhaling through the right, holding, exhaling through the left, and so on.

Do not force your breathing. If you forget which side you are on, or it is stressing you out, pause. Bring your breathing back to its natural rhythm and practise a couple of slow calm breaths. The aim of this breathing practice is to calm the mind and body, not to create anxiety.

CHAPTER 5

Guided Meditation

A guided meditation helps you follow a meditation without having to think. Listen to the voice and let it guide you through. It can take away some stress from meditation because you hand yourself over to following the guidance and instruction, rather than having to think it through yourself. The temptation, especially when you first start meditating, is to cut it short if you start thinking of other things, or to become stressed as you do exactly what you are trying not to do. However, listening to an actual voice to set the path for the meditation can take away some of that anxiety. It provides a supportive frame for your practice.

Record these meditations so that you can listen to them as you sit. Ask a friend who has a gentle voice or record it yourself. Ensure there are plenty of pauses to allow you to relax into the guidance given. Longer pauses are much better than ones that are too short and rush the meditation.

You can practise these either lying down or sitting. If you take your headphones to work, you can take 10 minutes to allow yourself to follow the meditation.

There are plenty of guided meditations that you can download from the internet or your phone, some of which are free.

Try this guided meditation sitting up and gazing softly at a flickering candle flame.

"Breathe in through the nose. Sigh out through the mouth.

Observe your breathing. The breath naturally flows in and out, without you doing anything. Notice how the body manages the balance between the inhale and exhale.

See in your mind's eye the breath passing through the body. Where does it go as you inhale? Notice it pass into the nostrils. Follow the flow as it fills up the belly, letting the belly and the chest slowly rise.

[PAUSE]

Notice now the exhale. The belly drops as the out breath travels up the body, taking out any toxins from the body, releasing them into the air.

Observe the healthy oxygen come into the body on an inhale. Feel the fresh, clean air pass through your organs – heart, lungs, brain, liver, kidneys, intestines.

[PAUSE]

If your mind wanders, gently bring it back to the focus.

Breathe in. Let the breath flow into the body. Exhale. Let the body expel any negativity.

Let your gaze rest on the golden flame.

[PAUSE]

Breathe naturally and easily. If your mind wanders, softly come back to the golden glow of the flame. Rest your gaze.

Gently reawaken your body and mind.

[PAUSE]

Feel your cushion or chair. Notice the feel of your clothes against your body.

Wiggle your fingers and toes. Shrug your shoulders.

Open your eyes, and remain sitting for a few moments longer.

Blow out the candle and be still for a moment. Straighten out gently.

Pause as you notice how your body feels. Come to standing and hold with you the calm and energy from the meditation for the rest of the day."

Adapt this next meditation for lying or sitting, whichever you prefer.

"Settle into your posture. Listen to the natural rhythm of your breathing.

[PAUSE]

Draw your attention to your spine.
Let your spine lengthen like a strong tree.

[PAUSE]

Allow a flood of soft light to flow through your body.

[PAUSE]

As you inhale this gentle light, allow it to flow to your toes, heels and ankles. Send the light to your knees and thighs. Let it rest where there is any tension.

[PAUSE]

Allow the light to travel along your arms to your fingers. Let it flow into your neck and ears. Feel the soft light bathing your eyes.

[PAUSE]

Soften your body with the golden light.
Let the spine remain firm.

[PAUSE]

If your mind wanders, gently bring it back to the body. Notice if there is energy in your body as it relaxes.

[PAUSE]

When you are ready, gently wriggle your fingers and toes. Stretch your body in any way that feels good.

[PAUSE]

Softly, turn to your right side, curled up in a foetal position. Rest here for a moment.

[PAUSE]

Slowly, come to sitting. Take a moment to allow the body to sit. In your mind, silently thank yourself for this relaxation meditation practice."

CHAPTER 6

Guided Visualisation

Your imagination is a powerful tool. Use it in a conscious, deliberate way to help your body and mind let go of all the day-to-day stresses. Allow yourself 10 or 15 minutes to imagine and visualise a tranquil setting. Allow yourself to indulge in this calm and peaceful place where both body and mind can deeply relax and rejuvenate.

This type of relaxation draws on all your senses – sight, taste, touch, hearing, smell.

Choose a setting that resonates with calm and tranquility for you. This might be a river bank with a gentle breeze, or a long, sandy empty beach. This place belongs to you. You can change it each time you practise visualisation, or you can return to the same one again and again.

Before you start, know what you are going to visualise to avoid indecision and internal chatter. Lie down or get into a comfortable sitting position. Gently close your eyes. Take a few moments to let your body go. Let your breathing be easy and natural.

Take a few slow, deep, belly breaths. As you breathe in, let your belly fill with oxygen; as you breathe out, let your belly push out the air from your body.

Let your attention carry you to the place you are imagining.

View it in your mind's eye.

What does it sound like? Listen silently to the sounds of this calm, restful place.

Let your body sink into the floor. If you find your mind wandering, that's ok. Bring it back to this place of quiet and stillness that belongs to you.

What does it feel like? Is there a gentle breeze against your body, or soft grass on your feet?

Take your time. There is no rush or race. Experience this special place in detail. Notice the colours, the textures, the sounds. Rest in this place and allow your body and mind to soak up its calm and tranquility.

When you are ready, let your mind bring you back to the present moment.

As you bring the visualisation to a close, allow your body to soak up the stillness of the relaxation. Take a gentle deep breath. Stretch or sigh out. Wiggle your fingers and toes. Give your shoulders a gentle roll. If you have been lying down, turn onto your right side in the foetal position and slowly bring yourself to sitting. Enjoy a moment of calm and rest in seated position.

Carefully bring yourself to standing and allow your body to completely relax.

"Gently close your eyes. Let your breathing come and go naturally.

[PAUSE]

Take a few moments to let your body go. Let your breathing be easy and natural.

Take a few slow, deep, belly breaths. As you breathe in, let your belly fill with oxygen; as you breathe out, let your belly push out the air from your body.

[PAUSE]

Take yourself to a stream. Notice the clear cold water. Imagine sitting by the edge of the stream on a soft grassy bank.

[PAUSE]

Notice how the water ripples and flows over shiny stones. Look at the soft rays of sunlight as they flicker on the ripples.

[PAUSE]

How does the water sound in the gentle breeze? What else can you hear? The soft breeze blows the grass. Can you feel the shiny green blades brush in the slight wind?

Visualise your body lying on the grass. Soak up other sounds. What is the effect of any movement from fluttering and flying insects. What sounds do they make? Notice the vibrancy of colours.

Immerse yourself in this peaceful oasis. Allow your body to be energised by the beauty of this cool, bright place.

Slowly and gently bring your focus back to the present. Notice the feel of the mat beneath you, the touch of your clothes. Notice the sounds in the room.

Slowly open your eyes. Bring movement back to your body, stretching out however you need to.

Come to a seated position. Invite the bliss from the visualisation to envelop your body and mind. Let it wash through you.

Feel the energy and calm from the relaxation. Hold it with you."

CHAPTER 7

Blissful Relaxation

Yoga is an ancient tradition of physical postures, called asanas, that work with the breath on both the body's frame and internal organs, helping the body to release tension and stress and find calm. The ancient art of t'ai chi has been practised in China for centuries. It combines smoothly flowing movements performed at a gentle pace, releasing tension in body and mind. The practice of t'ai chi balances the body, mind and energy (chi). Moves are not jerky or straight. They are fluid and curved.

Anyone can do yoga or t'ai chi. You don't need to be flexible or super fit. Most yoga postures can be modified to suit the individual, depending on his or her body. It is best to learn from a qualified instructor. There are lots of drop-in or longer courses. Ask if you can go for a taster session to see if it suits you.

If you are unused to exercise or have any fitness or medical concerns, check with your doctor first.

Sun Salutation

The sequence of poses that make up the 'Sun Salutation' help regulate the breath and focus the mind. The movements flow with the inhale and exhale. If anything hurts, stop.

Take time to find a strong standing pose with your hands together in front of your chest, pointing upwards. Check the balance of your weight is evenly distributed through your feet. Hold your core muscles tight.

Inhale and lift your arms above your head. Look gently towards your hands.

Exhale as you bend forwards. If your hands don't reach the ground, bend your knees.

Keep your hands where they are, inhale and stretch your right leg behind you. Gently drop your right knee to the floor. Arch your back and look up.

Hold your breath and bring your left leg back in line with the right, toes curled under. Keep your head and body in line, arms extended. If this is too hard, gently lower your knees to the floor.

Exhale and lower your knees to the floor, keeping your hips up, forehead low to the floor, or if you have the upper body strength, bend your elbows and lower your body.

Inhale as you slide your body forwards, lowering your hips and flattening your feet. Look up and back.

Exhale as you lift your hips and push back into your heels. Keep your head between your arms.

Inhale and bring your right foot in between your hands. Lower the right knee to the floor.

Exhale as you bring the left foot to join the right. Bend forwards.

Inhale reaching up and back.

Return to the standing pose and repeat on the other leg.

Bridge

This posture, called 'Bridge', creates a beautiful arch in your body.

Lie on your back with your knees bent, feet hip-width apart, hands gently by your sides. Breathe naturally.

Place your hands under your lower back.

Slowly lift your hips and chest.

Keep your feet parallel and flat on the ground.

Keep your head and neck on the ground.

Breathe deeply in the posture.

To come out of bridge, gently support your hips as you lower your body to the starting position.

Once you feel comfortable in this position, you can try variations, such as lifting one leg towards the ceiling from basic bridge. Make sure you repeat the moves with the other leg for balance.

The Tree

The pose known as 'The Tree' is a balancing posture. Balancing requires mental focus and physical strength. This helps the body maintain calm and stillness.

Find a fixed point on the floor in front of you, or on a wall. You can also use a wall as a gentle prop – stand about 30 centimetres away from it but put your hand out to it if you need to steady yourself.

Stand tall. Breathe deeply. Take a few moments to notice how your weight is distributed over your feet. Is your weight more in the balls of your feet, or the heels? Are you leaning to one side?

Find a centred stance. Bring your hands to prayer position, palms together in front of the chest.

Lift your left foot. Balance it against your right ankle. This might be enough for you. If you can, lift your left foot to rest against your right calf. Maintain a steady gaze at the fixed point. Hold your core strong and tight.

If you feel able, lift your left foot to rest against your inner thigh (not knee). Hold the position and breathe. If you wobble, that's fine. Try again. Repeat on the other side.

T'ai chi

You can sometimes see groups practising t'ai chi in parks. T'ai chi is an ancient martial art, today practised as a graceful form of exercise to release and align the body's internal energy. It involves a series of movements performed in a slow, focused manner and is accompanied by deep breathing. Each posture flows into the next without pause, ensuring that the body is in constant motion.

T'ai chi has many different styles, each of which has its own variations. The t'ai chi standing posture is known as 'wu chi' – meaning total emptiness.

It is designed to allow the flow of energy within you. Stand with your feet hip-width apart. Distribute your weight evenly. Rest your tongue gently on the roof of the mouth. Your chest and belly are relaxed, the front of the body sinks, the spine rising, arms to the sides with space in the armpits. Palms face backwards. Relax the knees. Face soft. Draw your chin back and slightly downwards.

The move known as 'Pouring' allows energy to bathe the body. Stand with your feet flat on the floor, parallel and shoulder-width apart. Notice how your body feels, grounded through your feet. Bend or pour your weight to your right side, bending one knee. Imagine emptying the weight from one side. Pour the weight to the other side, bending the other knee. Gently flow from side to side, allowing waves of energy to flow through the soles of your feet. Notice how it flows through the legs and upper body. As you shift weight to one side, fully release the weight from the other. Breathe, flow and relax.

CHAPTER 8

Mindful Eating

Mindful eating is about giving the same present attention to your body and what you eat, as you do to the breath or the focus of your mindful meditation.

How often do you gulp a drink on the go and grab a bite of a sandwich as you are doing something else? How often do you eat a main meal while watching TV or chatting to someone else? Eating mindfully is not something that we do often. But paying full attention to the action and experience of eating and drinking is rewarding, calming and nurturing.

Eating mindfully can help maintain a positive and healthy attitude to food. If we truly think about what we are eating, when we are eating and why, we may develop a less frantic approach to the nourishment that our bodies deserve.

Mindful eating is a focus on the here and now. It invites you to notice the colour of the food, its smell, its feel, its taste. What is the temperature of the food? What does it sound like as you bite on it? As random thoughts keep popping into your mind, let them go. Simply return to and focus on the act and experience of what you are eating in the present moment.

The regular practice of mindful eating will help you identify when you are hungry and when you are full.

How can one eat mindfully? Simple. By paying total attention to the act and experience of eating.

When you shop for food, know what you are going to buy. Be in the present moment as you select your food and place it in your trolley. Thoughts will come and go telling you to hurry up as you don't have time to linger in the shop, but just let those thoughts come and then go. Bring your focus back to the mindful approach.

When you are preparing food, do it mindfully. Engage your senses around the smell, taste, sound, feel and look of the food. Pay attention to the motion of chopping the food, or mixing it.

Instead of reaching to check messages on your phone as you eat your apple, just take a slow and conscious bite of the apple. Notice the colour of the apple skin. Look at the colour and texture of the apple flesh. Take a moment to smell the juice and freshness from the apple as you bite into it. Notice the sound of your teeth meeting the crunchy apple flesh. Feel the action of your jaw as your teeth sink in and bite. What does it feel like to chew the apple? Notice the process of the apple passing from your mouth into your stomach. As you take another bite, does it feel the same? Notice any changes. Be in touch with how each moment feels for you.

Realistically, you are not going to eat every mouthful of every meal mindfully. But you can aim to eat at least one meal a week with mindfulness. That means without music, the TV, a book or chatter. You can do this at work during your break or at home. Appreciate the stillness and pause that this mindful eating provides.

Of course, one can be mindful of how one eats, but it is also relevant to be mindful of what we eat as there are well-established links between food and mood.

Some foods cause a rush in energy that then crashes as quickly as it arrived. A slice of cake made with white flour and lots of sugar will give you a short energy burst followed by a dramatic loss of energy. This can feel stressful and lead to tension as you try to carry on with your busy day without enough fuel in your body to keep your energy levels at a consistent and calm level. Aim for a balanced diet in regular meals of fresh fruit and vegetables, protein, dairy and carbohydrates.

To encourage a reduction in stress and tension, the foods to avoid include:

Processed foods that contain additives and artificial chemicals.

Sugary drinks and foods that result in a short-lived energy burst.

Caffeine (in coffee) – great for a quick boost but it has been linked to worsening anxiety.

Instead, try to eat more of the following:

Salmon, tuna and other oily fish – they contain omega 3 that helps the function of the brain.

Proteins, including meat, fish, beans, lentils, tofu, eggs and cheese – these contain the mood-enhancing tryptophan, an essential amino acid that is converted into serotonin, a natural chemical in the body that is linked to mood.

Oats, wholegrains and protein keep your blood sugar steady to counter irritability, poor concentration and tiredness.

Brazil nuts – rich in the mineral selenium that has been linked to positive mood.

Almonds, spinach, cashews – high in magnesium that plays a role in the development of serotonin.

CHAPTER 9

Relaxation at Work

We need a certain amount of pressure at work in order to improve performance or remain motivated and challenged. However, too much pressure at work can create unhealthy stress that then has an impact upon home life as well.

It is clearly not practical to take half an hour of deep relaxation when you have no space to do so in a cramped staff room. There are ways, however, to introduce some relaxation time into your working day.

Think for a moment about your working week. What is rewarding, challenging and positive? What is causing stress that is impeding your performance rather than enhancing it, or causing anxiety and upset? Can you address or implement any change around the areas outlined on these pages? Identifying issues allows us to deal with problems more effectively and proactively. You may feel more swamped by a feeling of stress if you have not tried to identify its cause.

Working environment and conditions

Think about specifics that could improve your working life and give you less stress. It might be having a more comfortable chair or moving a computer into a better position. Employers have to take into account the health and safety requirements of their staff. If your place of work is incredibly noisy, is there anything you can do to minimise the noise?

Working hours

Shift work can be exhausting and play havoc with the body's natural rhythm and sleep patterns. Long hours are wearing. Perhaps you feel like you never stop working, and that working intrudes into your home life. Can you look at your working pattern and add in downtime for yourself? If you have a family to look after, perhaps you could talk to them about ways to give you more support. In practical terms, will you benefit from changing your working hours? If that is not practical or possible, how can you add in some time for rest and recuperation?

Colleagues

Personality clashes at work are very stressful. Is there anything on a practical level that you can do, such as talking to your manager or HR department? Are you able to change your approach towards a colleague so that the relationship becomes less tense?

The work

Are you ready for a change? Is it possible to change, or do you feel fixed to the job because of financial needs? If you are locked into the work but unable to leave, then it is very important to add in small details that are going to make it more bearable and thus easier for you to cope. Regular relaxation practice will help you to keep perspective and make you feel more in control.

Take 10 minutes to practise one of the breathing or visualisation techniques. Perhaps encourage a colleague to practise with you.

Lunchtime can be a luxury in some workplaces, but this should not be the case. You need to eat to fuel your body effectively. Take a lunchbox with nutritious foods that will give you the best energy and mood boost.

If possible, go for a walk. Fresh air and exercise are rejuvenating. If you have 10 minutes, practise mindful walking. Then sit quietly, perhaps meditating on the breath, practising mindfulness or visualisation. Listen to a guided visualisation on your headphones. Take a book to read for 10 minutes, to help you switch off from work.

Exercise is good for body and mind. As well as keeping you fit, exercise releases endorphins – powerful chemicals in your brain that energise and make you feel good. Can you go for a run or walk?

Could you play a sport for 20 minutes with colleagues?

During the day, find some moments of stillness. Stop – literally. Just take a few seconds to be still. If you question what you are doing, or should be doing, the answer is "nothing". The point of stillness is to return you to the present moment. Either focus on your breathing or on an object of stillness to which you can draw your attention.

If you are feeling overwhelmed by your work, turn off your phone and email for a set time. Think about the work tasks you need to do. Make a list, prioritise and feel in control.

Take mini breaks. Get up and move around. Do some simple stretches.

Talk to someone at work if all of the above ideas are not working for you. Your health and well-being at work is your employer's concern (and it is a legal obligation for them to address). Don't let work-stress pull you down.

CHAPTER 10

Relaxation at Home

Home is often a place full of busy times, with family, friends and domestic chores. It's important to introduce regular relaxation at home, but it is not always easy.

Chilling out with a glass of wine on an evening out or chatting in a café with friends is fun and a great way to switch off from stresses. It's important to note, however, the difference between this type of relaxation and the conscious relaxation techniques explored in this book.

Ideally, we would all have a haven of space in our home that is ours for relaxation. We could play gentle music there, close the door and know that we can remain undisturbed for 20 minutes. That is not possible for many of us, so have a few things that you can easily set up that help with the ritual and habit of conscious relaxation. Is there a cushion that you sit on or a blanket or mat that you regularly use? Light a candle to mark the start of your relaxation.

There will inevitably be noises that intrude upon your meditation practice, from traffic to slamming doors. Let the noises be there. Acknowledge them without following them and continue with your practice.

Daily relaxation

To begin with, certainly, it helps to set aside time for your relaxation practice. Early morning is good (you may need to get up 15 minutes early). It's a great way to set you up for the day ahead. Doing it first thing means you won't have to worry about fitting it in at the end of a busy day.

Ideally, you want to have a set time for relaxation practice, but you can draw on the techniques when you are doing other things.

Instead of getting frustrated or irritated as you wait in a queue or for an appointment, return to mindfulness or breathing exercises. If you are doing household chores, it is an ideal time to practise deep belly breathing.

You can be mindful washing up or putting clothes away. Slow down. Pay full attention to what you are doing in the here and now.

If you find yourself thinking and panicking about the million other things you have to do while you are washing up, gently acknowledge those thoughts and bring your focus back to the feel and experience of the water and soap suds as you wash a cup.

Turn the radio and TV off. Get rid of extra noise that is unhelpful and unnecessary. Silence is calming and soothing. If you are used to constant external noise, silence can feel quite alarming. Notice how it feels. Listen to your breath. Sit and listen to the silence.

Take time for a long, hot bath. It will relax your muscles as well as giving you some peace and quiet. Light some candles and add bubbles or essential oils to your bath. Sink into the feeling and take the time to enjoy. When you come out of the bath, try to be mindful and not rush into the next thing you have to do. Allow the feeling of calm to stay with you.

Creativity

As well as specific relaxation techniques, there are other things that you can introduce into your life in order to create more calm for yourself.

Get creative. You don't need to be good at drawing to enjoy the creativity of painting. Get some paints or felt tips and allow yourself the indulgence to create for 10 minutes. Think of it as doodling time. There are lots of colouring books for adults that are great stress-busters.

Get stuck into clay or play dough. Why keep it for the kids? Have you ever made your own bread? Forget a bread maker. Your hands will enjoy kneading the sticky dough. It is a great way to release pent up stress and to focus the mind. Try it.

A good book is a great way to switch off. Put your feet up and enjoy. Go to the library and choose some random books – see where they take you.

Light a candle, put on some soothing music, and just sit. Enjoy the sound.

Pick up a pen and paper. Write down your thoughts. Write a poem. Let the words flow without judgement. No one else needs to see them.

If you find it hard to switch off at home, join a class. There are lots of classes for adults from yoga to pottery. When you start yoga or t'ai chi, it is advisable to join a class taught by an experienced practitioner.

Massage

Touch is a beautiful, calming way to relax. It is wonderful if you can afford to have a qualified practitioner give you a massage but it's not always possible or practical. You can give and receive massages. These are some simple techniques you can practise easily on yourself.

Your eyes hold a lot of tension and do a lot of work. Give them a workout and rest with this palming technique that can be done anywhere.

Look up.

Look to the far right.

Look to the far left.

Look to the top right.

Look to the top left.

Look to the bottom right.

Look to the bottom left.

Circle your eyes clockwise and then anticlockwise.

Rub your palms together vigorously until they feel warm. Close your eyes. Firmly but gently cup your hands over your eyes (palms over the eyes, not the fingers).

Allow your eyes to enjoy the heat from your palms and the darkness. Breathe deeply.

The face holds a lot of tension. A quick self massage can be added to the start or end of one of the other techniques, such as breathing meditation or visualisation, or it can be done on its own.

Lie or sit. Gently close your eyes.

With your index and middle fingers make small circular motions following the line of your cheek bone.

With your index fingers, firmly make circular motions from the top of either side of the nose down to each nostril.

With your fingertips, lightly and softly stroke your eyelids, from the nose outwards.

Use your index finger to make circular motions on the dip in your chin.

Use both hands to make fluttery petal motions on all over your face.

Place a palm over each ear. Slowly use your hands to move your ears up and down in a circular motion. Hear the sound of the sea.

With both hands, use the tips of your fingers to press with circular motions all around your scalp.

The neck can hold a lot of tension. Take some time to practise this self-massage.

Lie on a towel or mat. Roll a small towel to fit directly under your neck, supporting it. Your head is resting on the ground. Relax the jaw and mouth.

Bend your legs, hip distance apart.

Slowly, roll your head to one side, keeping your head on the ground. Take a few deep breaths. Bring your head back to centre and repeat on the other side.

Gently hold the sides of the towel. Inhale and use your hands to bring your chin up towards your chest, supporting your neck in the towel. Exahle as you gently bring your head back to resting.

Need a break at work? A quick hand massage is easy to do and relaxing.

Stretch your hand out. With the other hand, use the thumb and index finger to rub each finger slowly in a firm but gentle circular pressure. Start at the base of the finger, working towards the tip. Hold the finger at the base, gently stretch it as you glide your grip up towards the fingertip and away from the finger.

Turn your hand so the palm faces upwards. Hold your hand between your thumb and fingers. Use your thumb to apply pressure on the palm and then wrist.

Stroke the back of your hand and squeeze all over.

Repeat on the other side.

Birthday coming up? Ask for a treat to have an aromatherapy massage. In addition, or alternatively, buy some essential oils and create your own aromatic relaxation. Our sense of smell can be activated for relaxation. You can buy lovely bubble baths but you can also use essential oils to create your own aroma for relaxation. Essential oils are the essences found in plants that give them their particular smell.

Research has shown that essential oils have an effect on the nervous system. As well as being calming, some can help provide all-important energy.

Safety

Do not drink an essential oil. If you spill some on your skin undiluted or have an allergic reaction, splash cold water over the affected area for 20 minutes. Some oils have contraindications. Check before using if you are unsure.

- Add a few drops to a bath, once it has run.
- Massage some diluted oil into the skin. Dilute the essential oil into a base oil such as almond or coconut oil.

- Make a room spray instead of using an artificial chemical concoction. Buy a plant spray and half fill with cold water. Add drops of your chosen oils and spray it around. Make one for work too. Citrus oils are refreshing. Lavender is particularly calming.
- Invest in a burner. Put some water and a few drops of your chosen oil into the burner plate. Light a tea candle underneath. Enjoy.

Top essential oils for relaxation

Ylang-ylang

Lavender

Bergamot (do not use on the skin 12 hours before going out in the sun as you will burn quickly)

Marjoram

Geranium

Clary sage

CHAPTER 11

A Personal Journey

The relaxation techniques in this book encourage you to empty your mind of the busy chatter of everyday life. It's not easy to do. And sometimes it can feel quite uncomfortable. Be kind to yourself in your practice. Relaxation is an ongoing process.

Sometimes a technique will feel ridiculously easy, and other times it might feel overwhelmingly hard. Don't judge yourself. Take time to think about the causes of stress and tension. Consider if you can take any control over this.

Top tips

- Be realistic. If you plan for relaxation techniques for an hour a day, it is unlikely you are going to sustain this.
- Expect ups and downs. Don't be discouraged if you miss a few days or even a few weeks. It happens. Just get started again and slowly build up to your old momentum.
- When you are tense, adopt a strong but relaxed posture. Roll your shoulders and let your jaw slacken. Tension starts here. Relax your jaw and tongue.
- Belly breathe! Use your breath to help you calm and to activate the relaxation response.
- To avoid fiddling or feeling stressed about what to do with your hands, hold your thumbs together and roll them around each other.
- Be kind to yourself. Allow thoughts to come and go when you are practising.
- Incorporate downtime in your life, such as watching TV or reading a book. Try to focus on one thing at a time.
- Enjoy snatches of silence and quiet. Take time to stop and smell the flowers.
- Whatever you do can be done mindfully.
- Notice what triggers tension and stress in all areas of your life. Can you do anything to reduce it?
- Make time for deep relaxation – it is an investment in your physical and mental well-being.
- Explore and enjoy!

Picture Credits

Interiors: all images courtesy of iStock: Andresrimaging 12, Billnoll 37, Susan Chiang 66, City_Mouse 15, Claudiad 85, Claudiaveja 83, Clicker 39, Coloroftime 11, DeanDrobot 77, deeepblue 87, Dima_sidelnikov 89, DRB Images, LLC 41, F9photos 96, Ferrantraite 30, Fizkes 44, Focusstock 4, Geber86 19, 78, GlobalStock 21, 43, G-stockstudio 75, Kadirkaplan 33, Klenova 72, Lilly3 67, LittleBee80 47, Luchschen 81, Nadya Lukic 62, Mallivan 29, Ian McDonnell 86, Mediaphotos 84, Michaeljung 93, Dean Mitchell 31, Mocker_bat 64, Monkeybusinessimages 69, Nankwei 32, Leonardo Patrizi 71, Pavel_ Markevych 95, PeopleImages 7, 22, 59, Pixdeluxe 53, Pkline 65, Alex Sava 35, Skynesher 40, Svetikd 9, Tassii 27, Romolo Tavani 13, Kais Tolmats 60–61, TPopova 20, Valio84sl 55, Xp3rt5 94, Yuri 17, 51, Peter Zelei 56, Zoliky 25.